M000267927

This book is about
A CAT
called

Nine Lives

THE CAT RECORD BOOK

Contents

From the Start

What is your cat's name?

....

Why did you choose this name?

....

....

....

Does your cat have a nickname?

....

When was your cat born?

....

What sex is it?

....

Photograph

From the Start

What breed is it? Is your cat typical of the breed?

....

....

....

....

....

How would you describe the type and colour of your cat's coat?

....

....

....

....

Does it have any special markings?

....

....

....

What colour are its eyes?

....

....

....

Do you know the details of your cat's parents?	
FATHER	**MOTHER**
Name	Name
Breed	Breed
Colour	Colour

4

From the Start

How many kittens were in the litter?

Do you know how many brothers and how many sisters your cat has?

Did you have a number of kittens to choose from? Why did you choose this particular one?

Who did you get your cat from?

Name:

Address:

Phone number:

Do you know the name and address of the breeder?

Name:

Address:

Phone number:

Life as a Kitten

How old was your kitten when you brought it home?

....

What does it look like? What sort of character does it have?

....

....

Does it have any unusual features or habits?

....

What sort of 'meow' and purr does your kitten have?

....

....

Photograph

When does it have its meals?

....

....

What food and drink do you normally give it?

....

....

Does it like any unusual foods?

....

....

Life as a Kitten

Does it need any special care?

Has it ever climbed the curtains? Has it ever damaged the furniture?

What special memories do you have of your kitten?

A kitten is the delight of a household.
All day long a comedy is played out
by an incomparable actor.
CHAMPFLEURY

Housetraining

How long did it take to housetrain your cat?

Were there any unfortunate accidents?

Does your cat use a cat flap?

If so, how long did it take to learn to use it?

Security

What type of collar does your cat
have?

Does it carry an identity disc?
If so what are the details on the
disc?

In a cat's eyes,
all things belong to cats.
PROVERB

Does your cat know its name? How does it respond when you speak to it?

Do you always call your cat in at the end of the day?

Character

Is your cat very independent?

Is your cat affectionate? Does it enjoy having a cuddle?

What is the character of its breed? How typical of the breed is your own cat?

Character

What habits (good and bad) does your cat have?

....

....

....

....

....

How would you describe its temperament? Does it get frightened by anything?

....

....

....

....

....

Photograph

Sleeping

Does your cat have a basket?

....

....

....

Where are its favourite resting places inside and outside your home?

Inside:

....

....

....

Outside:

....

....

....

Does it have a favourite chair?

....

....

....

....

Are there any unusual places where you have found it sleeping?

....

....

....

....

....

....

....

....

Sleeping

A sleeping cat is ever alert.
FRED SCHWAB

At what times of day does it usually sleep? Does it vary with the seasons?

Favourite Foods

At what times of day do you feed your cat?

....

....

What are its usual drinks?

....

....

How much food do you normally feed your cat?

....

....

....

Cats know how to obtain – food without labour,
shelter without confinement,
and love without penalties.
WALTER LIONEL GEORGE

Favourite Foods

Does it need a special diet?

....

....

....

Is your cat a fussy eater?

....

....

....

What are the foods you most often give it?

MAIN MEAL

....

....

....

MAIN MEAL

....

....

....

MAIN MEAL

....

....

....

What treats do you give your cat?

....

....

....

Play/Toys

As a kitten what were its favourite toys?

....

....

....

....

....

What are its favourite playthings now?

....

....

....

....

....

Does it have any favourite chasing and pouncing games?

....

....

....

....

....

....

....

Does your cat have an indoor scratching post?

....

....

....

....

....

Play/Toys

Does your cat ever watch television? Does it have a favourite programme?

Nothing's more playful than a young cat,
nor more grave than an old cat.
THOMAS FULLER

Territory

How far does your cat's territory stretch? Does it sit anywhere special to view its

domain?

....

....

....

....

....

....

....

....

....

Photograph

Territory

Does it challenge invading cats? All of them, or only some?

Does your cat use a favourite tree to sharpen its claws?

Hunting

*God made the cat
in order that man might have
the pleasure of caressing the tiger.*
FERNAND MERY

Is your cat a skilled hunter?

Is it a good mouser?

Does it like to stalk through the undergrowth?

Hunting

What does it catch?

Does it bring its catch/kills home to show you?

21

Nightlife

Do you allow your cat out at night?

Does your cat make a noise at night? Does it ever get into fights with other cats?

Does it go out searching for a mate?

Nightlife

Where does your cat shelter at night? Does it use different places, depending on the weather or time of year?

Do you think your cat sometimes goes and stays in other houses at night?

Favourite People

Are there people of whom your cat is particularly fond?

....

....

....

....

Is your cat a good companion to you?

....

....

....

....

....

Is it good with children?

....

....

....

....

....

Does your cat purr a lot? Does it rub up against you, or wrap itself around your legs?

....

....

....

....

....

Favourite People

Purring would seem to be, in her case,
an automatic safety-valve device
for dealing with happiness overflow.
MONICA EDWARDS

Is it friendly towards strangers out of doors?

Favourite People

How does your cat show its affection? Does it lick you?

....

....

....

....

....

....

....

Does it like being stroked?

....

....

....

....

....

....

Do you or any of your visitors have other pets? How does your cat behave with them?

....

....

....

....

....

....

....

Favourite People

Does your cat enjoy having a lot of people around it?

Photograph

Clean and Tidy

What type of coat does your cat have? Is it difficult to look after?

....

....

....

Does it groom and wash itself well?

....

....

....

....

For me, one of the pleasures
of cats' company is their
devotion to bodily comfort.
COMPTON MACKENZIE

Clean and Tidy

Does it have problems with fur balls?

Do you ever groom or comb your cat?

Do you ever use an anti-flea treatment on your cat? If so, what kind do you use?

Do you give your cat anything to help keep its teeth clean?

Do you ever check your cat's ears? Or its claws?

Adventures...

Is your cat a good climber?

Does it ever wander off for long periods?

Has it ever gone missing?

Has your cat ever gone exploring in the house and got stuck?

It has been the providence of Nature
to give this creature nine lives,
instead of one.

...and Narrow Escapes

Where does it hide when it feels threatened?

What dangerous situations has it got into? Does it seem to have luck on its side?

Does it try to look brave when in danger? Does it hiss or growl?

...and Narrow Escapes

Has your cat ever lost any of its 'nine lives'?

Has it ever been in, or caused, an accident?

Has it ever had to be rescued? Have you ever had to call anyone to help?

Holidays

Has your cat ever gone away with you on holiday? If so, where did you go and with whom?

Date:

Place:

With:

Date:

Place:

With:

Date:

Place:

With:

Does it enjoy going away?

Do your neighbours ever look after your cat?

Do you ever use a cattery if you go away?

Name:

Address:

Phone number:

Cost per day:

Holidays

No favour can win gratitude from a cat.
JEAN DE LA FONTAINE

Have you ever had to quarantine your cat? If so, when and where?

Other Cats

Does your cat get on with other cats? Are there any with whom yours is particularly

friendly?

Do you have any other cats yourself?

Photograph

Other Cats

What other cats have you had in the past?

Do other cats use your cat flap?

Have any other cats adopted you?

Parenthood

Has your cat ever had kittens?

What was the mate's breed, colouring and markings?

*A kitten is the most irresistible
comedian in the world.
Its wide-open eyes gleam
with wonder and mirth.*
AGNES REPPLIER

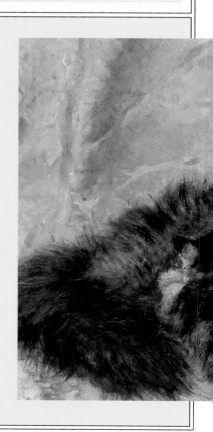

Parenthood

When was the litter born? Were you present?

Parenthood

There are no ordinary cats.
COLETTE

How many were there in the litter?
....

NAMES	COLOUR/MARKINGS	SEX

Parenthood

Do you remember when they were being weaned and reared? Was your cat an
affectionate parent?

What new homes did the kittens go to?

NAME of kitten	NAME & ADDRESS of new owner

Showing Off

Have you ever entered your cat for shows? What was the first occasion?

....

....

....

Does your cat like going to shows? Does it behave differently when on show? Has it ever misbehaved?

....

....

....

What is the most important show your cat has entered?

....

....

....

Has it won any prizes? If so, at which show, and where was it placed?

SHOW/CLASS	DATE	RESULTS/PRIZES

Showing Off

Do you have any show
ambitions for your cat?

A dog is a dog,
a bird is a bird,
and a cat is a person.
MUGSY PEABODY

What items do you take with you in the show bag? What grooming and preparation
does it involve?

Medical Record

What is the veterinary surgeon's name?
....
....
....

Name of practice:
....

Address:
....
....
....

Phone number:
....

What are the surgery hours?
....
....
....

List below the vaccinations which have been given to your cat and when.

| COMBINED VACCINATIONS AGAINST | | |
Feline infectious enteritis, Feline influenza and Feline leukaemia		
Age of Kitten	Date Given	Cost
9 weeks		
12 weeks		
Age of Cat	Booster Dates	Cost

Medical Record

Use the next three pages to compile the medical history of your cat.

WORMING TABLETS

Date Given	Cost

ILLNESSES/AILMENTS

Illness	Date	Cost

Medical Record

CHECK-UPS AND OTHER VISITS

Reason for Visit	Date	Cost

Medical Record

OPERATIONS		
Type of Operation	Date	Cost

Insurance

Do you have any medical insurance for your cat?

Which company is the insurance with?

Address:

Phone number:

Policy number:

Premium renewal date:

Annual premium:

CLAIMS	DATE	SETTLED

ALSO IN THIS SERIES
Faithful Friend – THE DOG RECORD BOOK

FOUR SEASONS
PUBLISHING LIMITED

Published in England by
FOUR SEASONS PUBLISHING LTD.
16 Orchard Rise, Kingston Upon Thames, KT2 7EY, England
Tel: 020 8942 4445
E-mail: info@fourseasons.net

Designed and typeset by Judith Pedersen
Printed in Singapore

ISBN 1 85645 133 X

ACKNOWLEDGEMENTS
Four Seasons Publishing Ltd would like to thank all those who kindly gave permission to
reproduce the words and visual material in this book; copyright holders have been
identified where possible and we apologise for any inadvertent omissions.

Front Cover and page 25: *A Sweet Tortoiseshell* CHARLES VAN DEN EYCKEN
Back Cover and page 43: *A Pampered Pet* HENRIETTE RONNER-KNIP
Title Page and page 35: *A Cat in the Window of a Cottage* RALPH HEDLEY
Page 7: *Kittens at Play* CHARLES VAN DEN EYCKEN
Page 9: *Watching* KAREN GEORGE
Page 13: *Kittens* HENRIETTE RONNER-KNIP
Page 14: *"Up to no Good"* LOUISE EUGENE LAMBERT
Page 17: *Les Chats Mechants* CHARLES VAN DEN EYCKEN
Pages 20/21: *The Overturned Basket* LEON CHARLES HUBER
Page 28: *Mother's Love* HENRIETTE RONNER-KNIP
Page 31: *Das Gartenzimmer* GOTTHARDT KUEHL
Pages 38/39: *Taking a Cat Nap* HENRIETTE RONNER-KNIP
Page 40: *The Proud Mother* CHARLES VAN DEN EYCKEN

All images supplied by Fine Art Photographic Library Ltd., with the exception of that on
the Title Page and page 35, which was supplied by The Bridgeman Art Library/Visual Arts
Library, and that on page 31, which was supplied by AKG Photo London.

"十一五"期间国家重点图书出版规划项目

 中国国家汉办重点规划教材

MONKEY KING CHINESE

美猴王汉语（幼儿）下

编著：刘富华　王巍　周芮安

翻译：邵壮

 北京语言大学出版社
BEIJING LANGUAGE AND CULTURE
UNIVERSITY PRESS

THE MONKEY KING

Sun Wukong, the Handsome Monkey King, is the hero of the Chinese literary classic *Journey to the West* (Wu Cheng'en, the Ming Dynasty). This novel was based on a true story of a famous Chinese monk, Xuan Zang (602 ~ 664). After years of trials and tribulations, he traveled on foot to what is today India, the birthplace of Buddhism, to seek for the Sutra, the Buddhist holy book. Finally he got the sutras and returned to China, or the Great Tang as was called at that time. He translated the sutras into Chinese, thus making contribution to the development of Buddhism in China.

In this novel, Buddha arranged for a monkey to become the monk's disciple and escort him, to ensure that he makes it to the west to get the sutras. The monkey called Sun Wukong, made the adventurous journey with Tangseng (the master), the other two disciples—Zhubajie (the pig-man) and Shaheshang (the monk) and Bailongma(the horse).

Sun Wukong was born out of a rock and fertilized by the grace of Heaven. In the Water Curtain Cave in the Mountain of Flower and Fruit, he was the King of the monkeys. Being extremely smart and capable, he learned all the magic tricks and *kungfu* from a Taoist master. He can transform himself into seventy-two different images such as a tree, a bird, a beast of prey or a bug as small as a mosquito so as to sneak into an enemy's belly to fight him or her inside out. Using clouds as a vehicle he can travel 108,000 *li* by a single somersault. The handsome Monkey King excelled in supernatural powers, defied hardships and dangers, and killed monsters. He protected his master Xuan Zang to overcome the eighty-one difficulties in fourteen years of the journey, and finally attained the Buddhist scriptures. The Monkey King who is omnipotent, brave and winsome, is deeply beloved by Chinese children and adults alike even up till now.

Contents

To Our Teachers

Monkey King Chinese(preschool edition) is a series of elementary Chinese language primers for preschool children in English-speaking countries. It has two volumes. Each volume consists of six lessons, and each lesson has five to seven words and expressions, five exercises and one nursery rhyme.

The teaching objective of this book is to help children achieve a basic understanding of the pronunciation of the Chinese language and learn some basic Chinese words indicating objects that children are familiar with .

One feature of this series is that words are presented in *pinyin* in line with the learning characteristics and acceptability of the children from English speaking countries. Another feature is that attention has been given to develop preschool children's other abilities in the process of learning the Chinese language, therefore, various exercises and activities are included, such as maze, paper cutting, and games etc.

Suggestions to the teacher:
1. The teacher may give some preliminary explanation to the exercises in each lesson and then allow the children to express freely.
2. The task of the teacher is to guide the children to learn Chinese through fun activities.
3. It is not necessary for the children to be able to write *pinyin*. Imitating pronunciation and the games are the main instructional activities in class.
4. The new words in each nursery rhyme may be substituted with other new words of the lesson. The teacher may arrange other class activities and performances based on the nursery rhyme.

It is our hope that *Monkey King Chinese* will help the teacher lead children into the exciting world of the Chinese language.

WE LOVE SPORTS

lánqiú

pīngpāngqiú

huábǎn

hànbīngxié

jiànzi

gǎnlǎnqiú

1. Match the articles with the players.

lánqiú

•　　　•

gǎnlǎnqiú

•　　　•

pīngpāngqiú

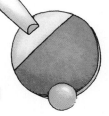

•　　　•

hànbīngxié

•　　　•

Monkey King Chinese

2. John's father has prepared a birthday gift for him. He would get the gift if he can find his way out the maze. What will the gift be? Circle the right picture below after you get out of the maze.

gǎnlǎnqiú

jiànzi

huábǎn

hànbīngxié

LESSON 1 **WE LOVE SPORTS**

3. Cut out the articles from the paper–cut area. Then paste them on the shaded areas.

gǎnlǎnqiú

lánqiú

huábǎn

pīngpāngqiú

4. Link the identical sports goods below.

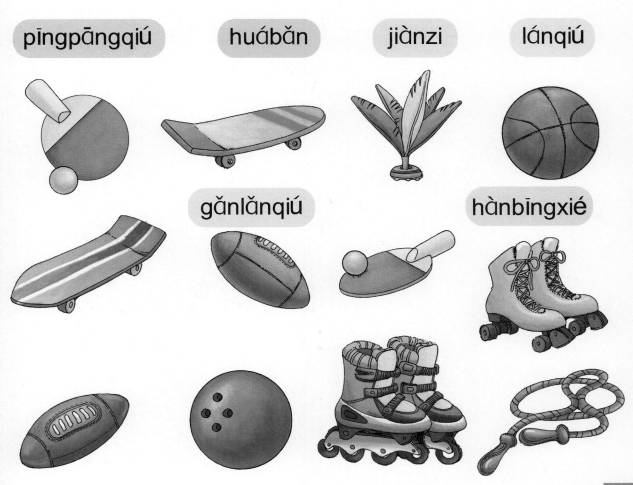

pīngpāngqiú　　huábǎn　　jiànzi　　lánqiú

gǎnlǎnqiú　　hànbīngxié

5. Find the differences between the two pictures.

huábǎn

Monkey King Chinese

Bàba yǒu lánqiú,

māma yǒu jiànzi.

Bǎobao yǒu shénme?

Wǒ yǒu gǎnlǎnqiú.

Papa has a basketball,
Mama has a shuttlecock.
But what does the baby have?
I have a rugby ball.

I AM A LITTLE DRIVER

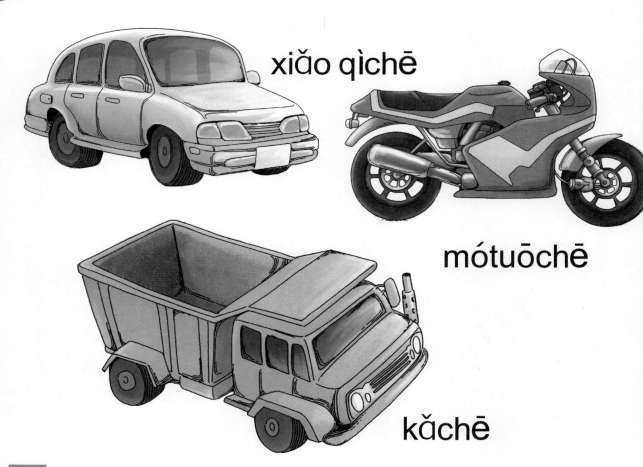

xiǎo qìchē

mótuōchē

kǎchē

jípǔchē

gōnggòng qìchē

huǒchē

11

1. Link the dots into lines and then color them.

kǎchē

xiǎo qìchē

Monkey King Chinese

2. **What are the missing parts of the vehicles below?**
Please complete them.

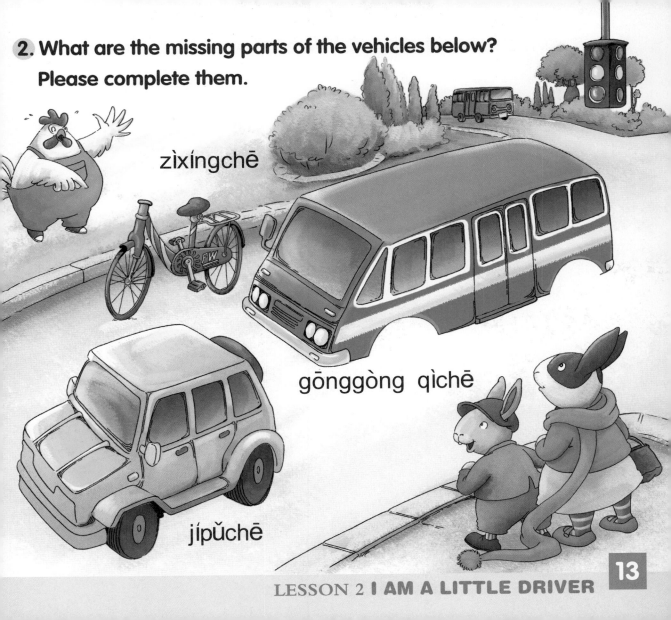

zìxíngchē

gōnggòng qìchē

jípǔchē

3. Count the number of each kind of the vehicle. Then write the numbers in the circles.

kǎchē

xiǎo qìchē

mótuōchē

zìxíngchē

Monkey King Chinese

4. Draw the same pictures as the given examples.

jípǔchē

xiǎo qìchē

5. Choose the appropriate vehicles for these people or goods and link them.

mótuōchē

kǎchē

gōnggòng qìchē

Lùshang chē zhēn duō,

lùshang chē zhēn duō.

Zhè shì shénme chē?

Zhè shì xiǎo qìchē.

So many vehicles in the street,
So many vehicles in the street.
What vehicle is this?
This is a car.

COLORFUL SEASONS

căihóng

chūn

xià

qiū

xuě

dōng

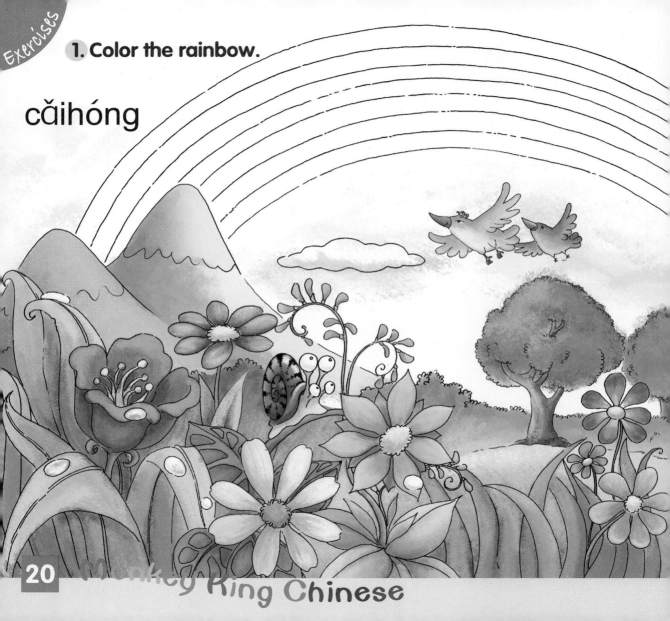

1. Color the rainbow.

cǎihóng

Monkey King Chinese

2. Guess the seasons according to the changes of the trees. Then link them.

chūn   xià   qiū   dōng

3. **Choose the right snowflake stickers according to the outlines of the snowflakes given below and paste them in the corresponding outlines.**

xuěhuā

4. Look at the pictures of the four seasons. Then cut out the right *pinyin* paper–cuts and paste them in the blanks of the right pictures.

5. Choose appropriate clothes for the little boy according to the season. Then draw the clothes on body.

 xià qiū  dōng  chūn

Monkey King Chinese 美猴王汉语(幼儿)下　剪贴页

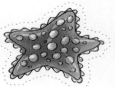

Chūn jiù shì chūntiān,

chūntiān zhēn měilì.

Wǒmen ài chūntiān,

wǒmen ài sìjì.

Chun is spring,
How beautiful spring is!
We love spring,
We love the four seasons.

IN THE VEGETABLE GARDEN

qiézi

nánguā

xīhóngshì

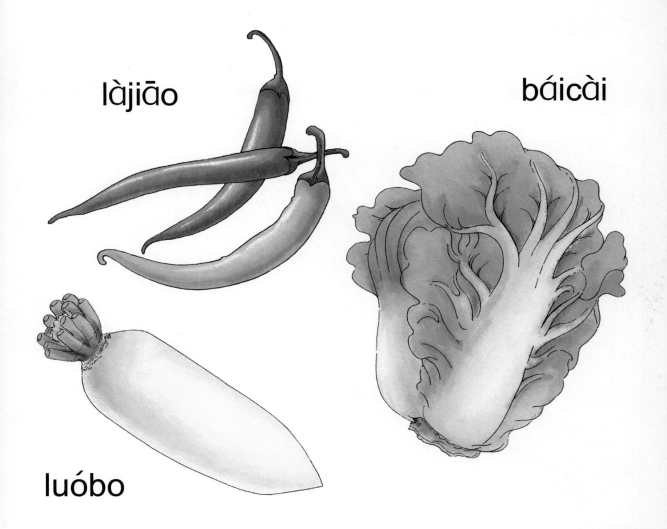

làjiāo

báicài

luóbo

1. Complete the pictures by coloring.

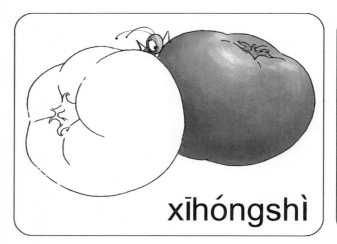

xīhóngshì

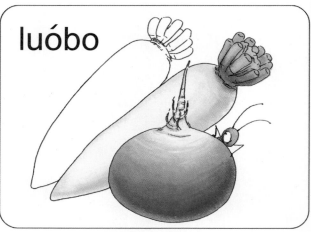

luóbo

làjiāo

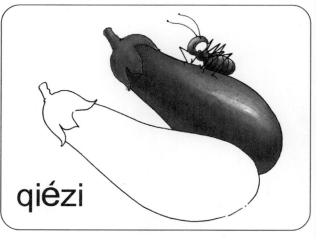

qiézi

Monkey King Chinese

2. Look at the picture in the first row. Then cut out the picture and paste them on the right blanks in the second and the third row with the aid of the pictures in the first row.

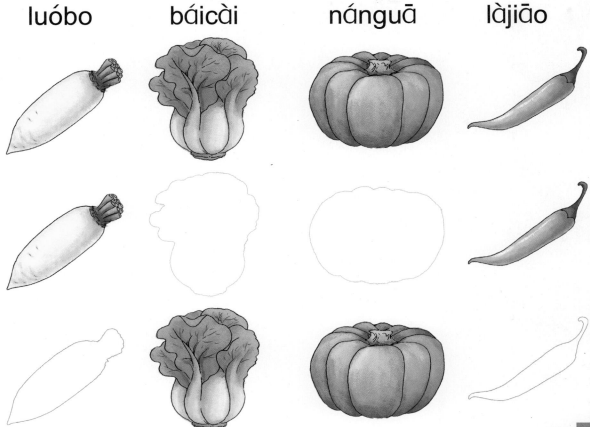

luóbo   báicài   nánguā   làjiāo

3. **Match the vegetable slices with the right vegetables.**

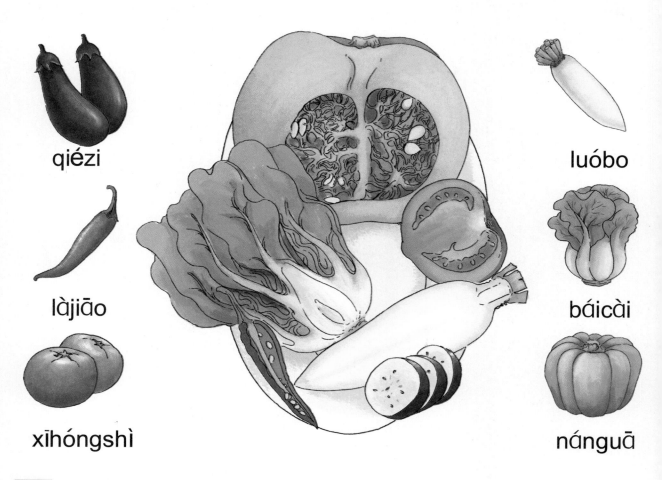

qiézi

làjiāo

xīhóngshì

luóbo

báicài

nánguā

Monkey King Chinese

4. Find the "hot peppers" and the "tomatoes" in the picture and link them with their *pinyin*.

làjiāo   xīhóngshì

5. How can the delivery men deliver their vegetables to their buyers? Draw the right route in the maze by using crayons.

Xiǎo péngyou,

ài chī cài.

Chī shénme?

Chī báicài.

Little kids,
Like eating vegetables.
What are they eating?
They are eating Chinese cabbage.

FRIENDS IN THE SEA

jīngyú

hǎixīng

hǎiguī

Monkey King Chinese

hǎitún

qǐ'é

pángxiè

1. Look at the outlines of some marine animals below. Then find the right animals in the sticker area and paste them in their outlines.

jīngyú

hǎixīng

hǎiguī

qǐé

2. Observe the pictures. Then draw the same picture on the right.

qǐ'é

hǎiguī

3. Link the red dots into lines and color it, and see what kind of marine animal you will get.

pángxiè

4. Cut out the marine animal paper–cuts. Then paste them below the right *pinyin* according to the numbers given on the left.

jīngyú

2

hǎixīng

4

hǎiguī

3

5. Find the differences between the two pictures below.

hǎiguī   hǎixīng   pángxiè

Monkey King Chinese

Dàhǎi dà,

dòngwù duō.

Yǒu shénme?

Yǒu qǐ'é.

The sea is big,
And there are many marine animals in it.
What does it have in it?
It has penguins.

GRANDMA'S ROOM

biǎo

bēizi

yǎnjìng

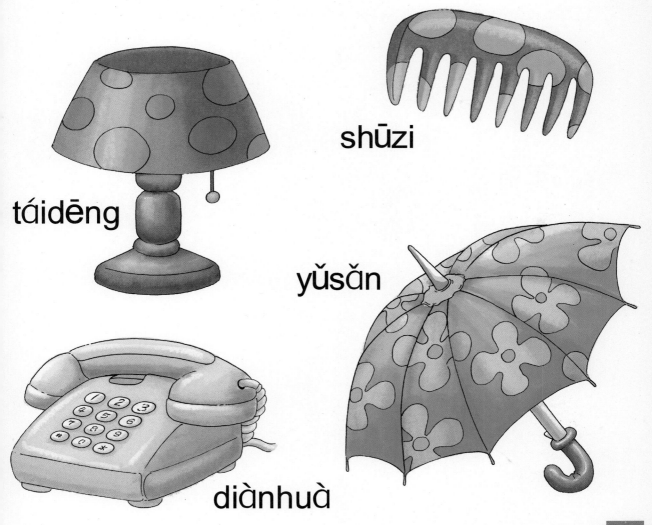

tÃ¡idÄ“ng

shÅ«zi

yÇ”sÇŽn

diÃ nhuÃ

43

1. Match the pictures with the relevant articles.

·   ·   ·   ·

·   ·   ·   ·

yǎnjìng   shūzi   biǎo   yǔsǎn

Monkey King Chinese

2. Draw to complete the pictures below.

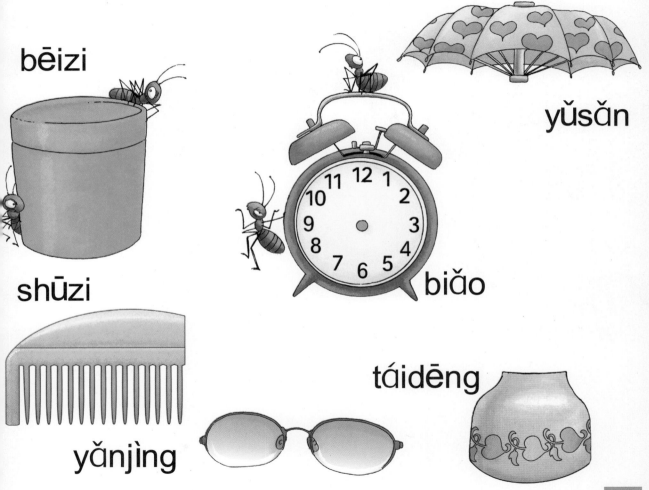

bēizi

yǔsǎn

shūzi

biǎo

táidēng

yǎnjìng

3. Find the right stickers and then paste them on the right place according to the *pinyin*.

táidēng

bēizi

diànhuà

yǔsǎn

Monkey King Chinese

4. Find the same picture in each row as the example. Then draw a circle on it.

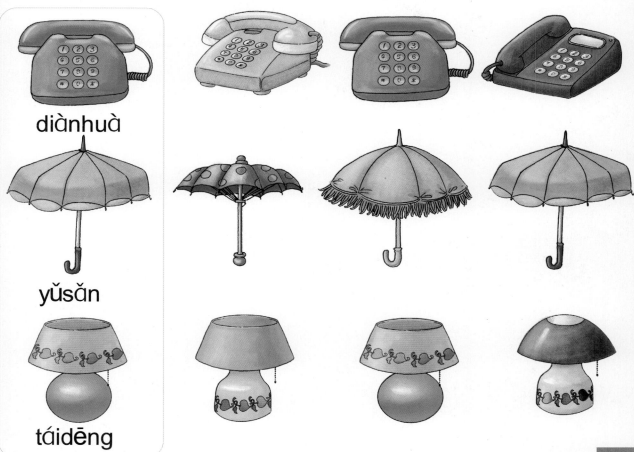

diànhuà

yǔsǎn

táidēng

5. Count the number of the combs, watches, cups and glasses.
Then write the numbers in the circles.

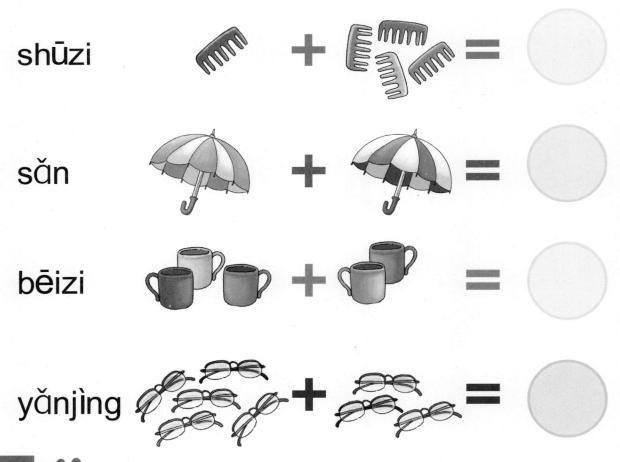

Monkey King Chinese

Lǎo nǎinai, zhēn zháojí,

bēizi bēizi zài nǎli?

Bēizi bēizi zài zhèli,

zhǎodào bēizi xiàomīmī.

Old granny is really worried.
Where is the cup? Where is the cup?
Here it is. Here it is.
So a chearful smile is on her face.

VOCABULARY

篮球	lánqiú	毽子	jiànzi
橄榄球	gǎnlǎnqiú	滑板	huábǎn
乒乓球	pīngpāngqiú	旱冰鞋	hànbīngxié

卡车	kǎchē	公共汽车	gōnggòng qìchē
小汽车	xiǎo qìchē	吉普车	jípǔchē
摩托车	mótuōchē	火车	huǒchē

春	chūn	冬	dōng
夏	xià	雪	xuě
秋	qiū	彩虹	cǎihóng

茄子	qiézi	白菜	báicài
南瓜	nánguā	辣椒	làjiāo
西红柿	xīhóngshì	萝卜	luóbo

海豚	hǎitún	螃蟹	pángxiè
鲸鱼	jīngyú	企鹅	qǐ'é
海龟	hǎiguī	海星	hǎixīng

杯子	bēizi	电话	diànhuà
眼镜	yǎnjìng	梳子	shūzi
表	biǎo	伞	sǎn
台灯	táidēng		

图书在版编目(CIP)数据

美猴王汉语(幼儿).课本 B/刘富华等编著.—北京：北京语言大学出版社,2009 重印
ISBN 978 - 7 - 5619 - 1656 - 8

Ⅰ.美…　Ⅱ.刘…　Ⅲ.汉语 – 对外汉语教学 – 教材　Ⅳ.H195.4

中国版本图书馆 CIP 数据核字(2006)第 062950 号

书　　名：	美猴王汉语（幼儿）. 课本 B
责任编辑：	张程　王昕
绘画设计：	
责任印制：	汪学发

出版发行：**北京语言大学出版社**

社　　址：北京市海淀区学院路 15 号　邮政编码：100083
网　　址：www.blcup.com
电　　话：发行部　82303650 /3591 /3651
　　　　　编辑部　82303647
　　　　　读者服务部　82303653 /3908
　　　　　网上订购电话　82303668
　　　　　客户服务信箱　service@blcup.net
印　　刷：北京外文印刷厂
经　　销：全国新华书店

版　　次：2006 年 9 月第 1 版　2009 年 4 月第 3 次印刷
开　　本：787 毫米×1092 毫米　1 / 24　印张：2.5
字　　数：11 千字　印数：13001—19000 册
书　　号：ISBN 978-7-5619-1656-8 / H·06104
　　　　　03000

凡有印装质量问题，本社负责调换。电话：82303590